Shhh...
Good
Night

Written by
Nicky Benson

Illustrations by
Thomas Elliott

Good night my love,
it's time to rest,
Watch amber skies
turn grey...

Mama bird
quiets her nest,
At the ending
of the day.

Shhh, baby bird.

Leaves rustle,
squirrels scurry,
Collecting nuts
and seed...

Bedtime's coming
in a hurry,
Rest is what
they need.

Shhh, baby squirrel.

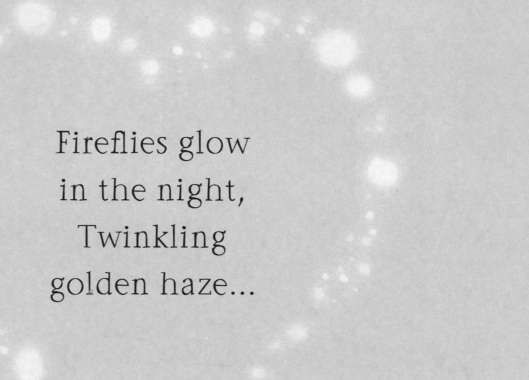

Fireflies glow
in the night,
Twinkling
golden haze...

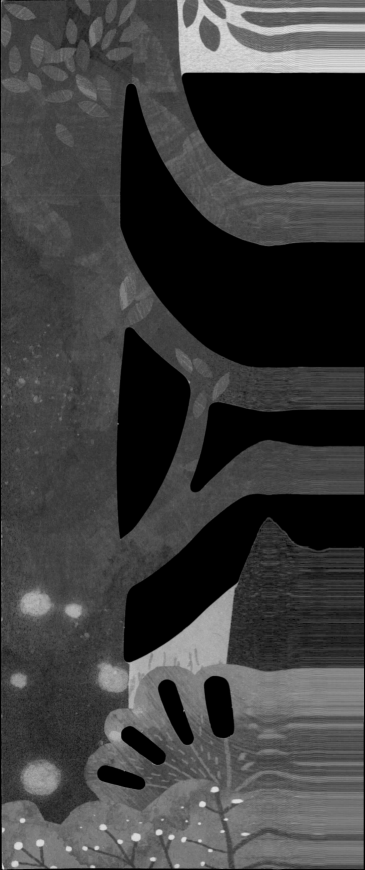

Shhh, baby squirrel.

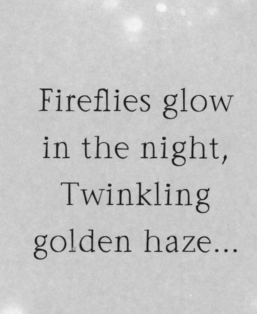

Fireflies glow
in the night,
Twinkling
golden haze...

Shhh, baby firefly.

Time for bed,
little deer,
Quiet sounds
and mind...

Settle down,
snuggled near,
Dreams are
what you'll find.

Shhh, baby deer.

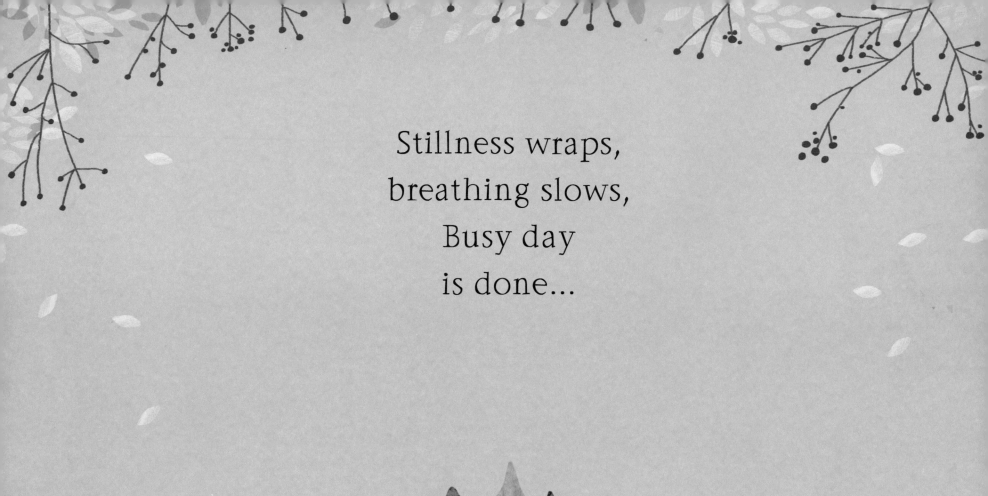

Stillness wraps,
breathing slows,
Busy day
is done...

Eyelids drift,
slowly close...
Good night,
everyone.